D1103914

Stereogram book of ROCKS MINERALS & GEMS

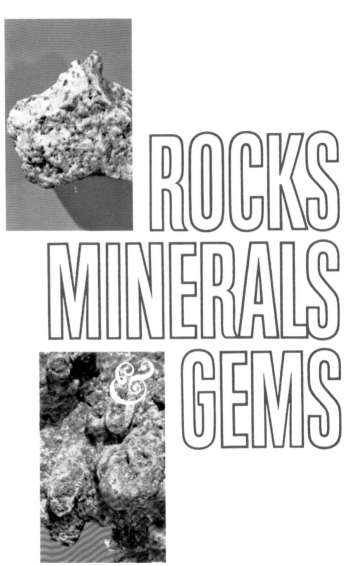

Text by David Techter

Curator of Natural Sciences, Geology

Rochester (N.Y.) Museum and Science Center

Special Consultant: Dr. Edward Olsen

Curator of Mineralogy

Field Museum of Natural History

Photography by Arch McLean

HUBBARD

Table of Contents

Introduction

The goals in the basic study of rocks and minerals for either students or simply an interested observer and collector can vary considerably. One aim, however, is uniform throughout all such study: to familiarize the student or observer with the 50 to 100 minerals and rock types that are most common on earth, and to make him aware of at least an additional 50 to 100 which are less common but still not considered rarities.

The process of becoming familiar with rocks and minerals involves the ability to apply a series of observations and tests. The first observation each person automatically makes is to mentally note how a certain specimen "looks" and simultaneously what it "looks like." Looks are difficult to define. They are the sum of a host of visual properties—color, shape, luster, fracture and cleavage patterns, characteristic blotches of stain, and so forth—which are grasped in a glance and stored in the mind for future reference. Experienced geologists working in the field, where conditions normally do not permit extensive tests to be made on a specimen, rely heavily on "looks" to make identifications and determine whether a given specimen is interesting enough to save or to send back for further laboratory testing. Hence, it is important for an active observer to have a basic mental file of rocks and minerals as well as their properties and characteristics.

Book Design by Don Walkoe

168798

Copyright © 1970, 1971, 1972
Hubbard Scientific Company, Chippewa Falls, WI 54729

Printed in the United States of America.

At one time most universities maintained two kinds of collections. The *classroom* collection consisted of common occurrences of minerals and rocks to be handled, tested and gradually expanded. The *study* collection consisted of better quality specimens (good crystal form, etc.) as well as examples of some less common specimens. These were to be carefully handled and examined, and then returned to a permanent and not easily accessible collection.

Today most colleges and universities as well as individual collectors find it difficult to put together complete study collections of high quality specimens. Older schools often have collections that were established decades ago, and schools initiating an earth science or geology curriculum must start from scratch. Minerals of study-specimen quality are rare, expensive and sometimes not even available.

The *Stereogram Book of Rocks, Minerals and Gems* is designed to provide a highly accessible and graphic collection of study specimens. The ability to view high-quality specimens in three dimensions enables the investigator to study rocks and minerals to a degree just short of having the actual specimens, and much more effectively than any ordinary single dimension publication could provide.

Hubbard Scientific has employed in this book a technique which it has used successfully in other investigative science publications. Each plate is presented as a stereo pair, that can be viewed through the stereo glasses as a three-dimensional specimen illustrating form, shapes, structure, and dimensional characteristics. Crystal shapes with their characteristic terminating faces or cleavages, for example, are features that cannot be adequately shown in a flat photograph no matter how cleverly lighted and shadowed. In producing these stereo photographs every precaution was taken to insure correct color representation of the specimen by the control of background colors and lighting. The *Stereogram Book of Rocks, Minerals, and Gems* is aimed at both the student with his classroom needs and the independent collector, who may either be beginning his collection or seeking a book to increase his sources for mineral identifications.

The specimens used in this volume were selected from the extensive museum study collection at the Field Museum of Natural History, Chicago, Illinois. Care was taken to choose specimens that illustrate good crystallization, sharp and true color, and distinctive characteristics. Specimens which were considered atypical in some visual aspect were avoided. Every attempt was made to provide the kind of coverage a person would obtain by examining a good, established study collection.

In addition to the rocks and minerals, examples of the better-known gemstones, faceted and in-the-rough are included. The use of certain minerals as gems is a legitimate aspect of mineralogy and one that is infrequently considered in mineralogical texts. It is nevertheless of interest to the student and collector and it is logical to include an investigation of cut and uncut gemstones in the overall process of studying rocks and minerals.

The book also includes four stereograms of lunar rock formations (Appendix I). The four close-up photographs were taken on the moon by the Apollo 11 astronauts with a stereo camera, specially developed to take detailed stereo photos of a three-inch square surface area of the moon. The stereograms with their descriptions provide a unique basis for comparison of Earth and moon rock formations, and enable detailed study of lunar rocks and minerals in three dimensions.

Appendix II illustrates the six crystal systems in three dimensions so that this aspect of minerals can be understood more clearly and to provide an immediate frame of reference. The crystal system for each mineral is identified at the end of each mineral stereogram caption.

It is hoped that this book will make many rocks, minerals and gemstones familiar to the reader and enable him to observe and study high quality specimens that he might not otherwise have the opportunity to examine.

Dr. Edward Olsen
Curator of Mineralogy
Field Museum of Natural History

USING THE STEREOSCOPE

The stereogram pairs of photos are carefully mounted so that they can be viewed in three dimensions with any lens stereoscope or stereo glasses. Stereoscopes may vary in construction (some have legs, others do not) but the basic method of use is the same.

To view a stereogram pair of photos, the stereo glasses should be positioned so that the center or bridge of the glasses is directly above the space between the two photos. The center of each lens should be aligned with a common point in each photo. Then, as you look through the glasses, adjust their position until the two photos merge into one three-dimensional illustration. It may require a few seconds for the viewer's eyes to focus on the photographs, and perhaps slight adjustment of the glasses, before the picture will appear in sharp dimension.

The page that is being viewed should also be held flat to prevent any distortion. If the stereo glasses are mounted on legs, they should be held at the bottom of the legs so that the pressure of the viewer's hands resting on the page will keep it adequately flat.

ROCKS

The Earth is an immense ball of rock with its weight estimated at 6.6 sextillion tons. Hundreds of different rock types, resulting from the action of the Earth's tremendous natural forces, are the substance and mosaics of this giant sphere. The rock types vary in composition; but all consist of a mineral or mixture of minerals and some contain sediments and the fossilized remains of plants and animals.

Rocks are classified in three major groups—igneous, sedimentary and metamorphic—a classification that is based on the natural process by which the rock was formed. The stereograms in this chapter are grouped accordingly and illustrate the features of hand specimens of the most common varieties of the three rock groups.

Individual rocks, however, are the products of their environment, and are altered by the various natural forces to which they are exposed. The appearance of different specimens of one rock type, therefore, may vary considerably; so much so that they may have little if any visual similarity. A clear example would be the wide variety of colors and textures exhibited by such rocks as granite, gneiss and limestone.

The color and texture of individual rocks is the result of a multitude of factors. The original color of the constituent minerals may be masked by secondary staining through ground water activity. The cementing material in sedimentary rocks may alter the original color. Weathering and erosion may decay the rock, altering the chemical composition of the minerals and thus radically changing the texture and color of the original rock.

The specimens appearing in the following stereograms are fresh and unweathered. The same rock when exposed to the elements could look quite different. The examples, however, are typical and display striking characteristics of the basic type of rock they represent.

The rocks shown at the left are (from the top): granite, oolitic limestone, obsidian, phyllite and breccia.

IGNEOUS ROCKS

Igneous rocks are those that have crystallized or solidified from an originally molten rock material called *magma*. The vast majority of igneous rocks solidify beneath the Earth's surface and are called *intrusive*. Those that solidify above the Earth's surface, such as volcanic lava, are referred to as *extrusive*.

The rocks classified as igneous are further subdivided by their chemical composition and by their texture. Those with a relatively high silica content, light in both color and weight, are called *acidic*. The darker, heavier igneous rocks that are rich in iron and magnesium are termed *basic*. An additional feature in regard to texture is that the grain size of an igneous rock can range from large, such as pegmatite, to microscopic, as in basalt.

Igneous rocks with a crystal size greater than one millimeter are called *phaneritic*, while those smaller or with no crystal are *aphanitic*. Larger crystals called *phenocrysts* are sometimes surrounded by a *groundmass* of smaller crystals and produce *porphyries*, such as the granite porphyry in this chapter.

Pegmatite   This rock form normally occurs in wide veins that cut across other igneous masses. Pegmatite is usually similar in chemical composition to granite, but is characterized by large well-formed crystals. This specimen is from the Petaca district of New Mexico.

Granite   The most abundant igneous rock is granite. Its color can vary considerably, depending on the proportions of orthoclase feldspar (generally pink, as in this specimen) to plagioclase feldspar (white, yellow, or gray) and the amount of biotite (black) present in the rock. The sample was taken from Moose-a-bec, Maine.

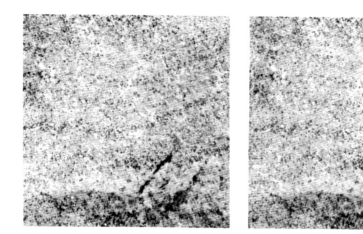

Syenite The dominant mineral in syenite is orthoclase. Syenite differs from granite in that it lacks quartz, as a result of the low silica content in magma. This specimen is taken from Lyon Mountain Iron Mine, Lyon Mountain, New York.

Felsite Felsite is *aphanitic* rock, one in which the constituents cannot be seen with the unaided eye. Most felsite rocks resemble granite or syenite in chemical composition. Many lava flows are also felsite. This specimen was found at Dannemora, Sweden.

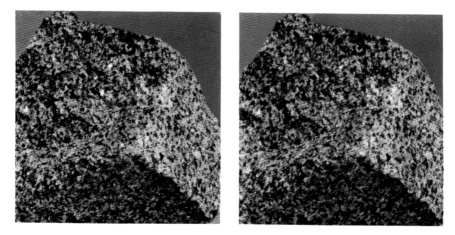

Diorite This type of igneous rock is composed of plagioclase feldspar, biotite, hornblende, and pyroxene, with virtually no quartz present. Pyroxene and plagioclase predominate in this sample of diorite found at Central City, Colorado.

Gabbro   Many of the large intrusive masses of gabbro contain ore bodies of iron and/or titanium. Gabbro differs from diorite in that the ferromagnesian minerals (pyroxene, hornblende, and olivine) are more abundant than plagioclase feldspar. This sample is from Germany.

Anorthosite   This rock form is composed almost entirely of plagioclase feldspar (anorthite or labradorite). It is not a common rock, but is found in plentiful amounts in eastern Canada and the Adirondack Mountains of New York. This specimen was found at Lake Sanford, New York.

Peridotite   Olivine is the predominant material in peridotite, with traces of biotite and pyroxene also present in this dark, heavy intrusive rock. Some peridotites contain sufficient chromite to be valuable ores of chromium. This sample is from Murfreesboro, Arkansas.

Granite porphyry   A porphyry carries the name of its matrix or groundmass (granite porphyry, basalt porphyry, etc.). This specimen is a granite porphyry in which phenocrysts of feldspar and quartz occur within a groundmass composed of the same minerals plus hornblende. It was found in France.

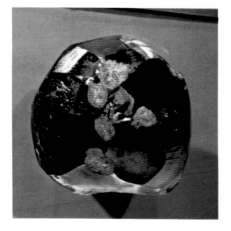

Obsidian   This extrusive igneous rock is lava that cooled too quickly to permit crystal formation. The result is natural glass, typically jet black. Thin fragments of obsidian, however, are transparent. This specimen is from Union County, Oregon.

Obsidian   This specimen illustrates the typical conchoidal fracture of the natural volcanic glass. Primitive peoples, especially in ancient Mexico, fashioned this form of obsidian into knives, arrowheads, and other implements. The sample was taken from the Lipari Isles, Sicily.

Rhyolite The fine textured form of lava, rhyolite, is similar in composition to granite. It is usually characterized by an aphanitic groundmass and phenocrysts of orthoclase. Phenocrysts of both rhyolite and andesite are frequently very small and megascopic identification is difficult. This example is from Durango, Mexico.

Andesite A form of lava, andesite corresponds in composition to diorite. The sample has an aphanitic background and phenocrysts of plagioclase. Andesite gets its name from the Andes Mountains, an area that is rich in deposits of this rock. This example was uncovered at Mohorn, Germany.

Basalt This aphanitic rock corresponds in composition to gabbro. Basalt is common both as lava and as intrusive rock associated with volcanism. Another common name for basalt is "trap rock," particularly used to identify the rock when it is crushed for roadfill or other uses. This specimen is from Wachenheim, Germany.

Lava　The most common extrusive rock is lava. This specimen is one form—basaltic lava; it shows gas bubbles and ropy flow structures (known as *Pahoehoe*). It was recovered from Mount Kilawea, Hawaii, currently one of the most active volcanos in the world.

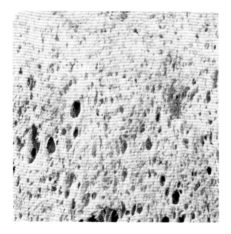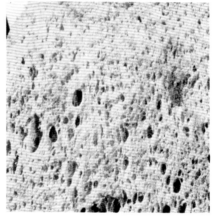

Pumice　This highly porous rock is formed when escaping gasses from volcanic activity froth up liquid lava. The resulting glass froth is extremely light and buoyant. This specimen is from the Lipari Islands off the northeast coast of Sicily, an area of highly active volcanism.

Scoria　This volcanic product is formed in the same manner as pumice, but from a more viscous lava (usually basaltic in composition). Because of this, scoria has an irregular slag-like texture. This example is from the Popocateptl Volcano, Mexico.

SEDIMENTARY ROCKS

Sedimentary rocks are those that have consolidated from sediments, materials that have been eroded from existing rocks by the action of weathering and other geological processes, and then were deposited in layers. Sediments such as sand, gravel, silt, and mud, subjected to physical and chemical actions as a result of being buried under later sediments, eventually solidify as sedimentary rocks. Because of the different grain sizes in sediments, there are corresponding gradations in sedimentary rocks.

Sedimentary rocks are usually grouped into *clastic* and *non-clastic* rocks. Clastic rocks are those formed by the consolidation of particles of rock matter produced by erosion: gravels become conglomerate or breccia; sand forms sandstone; mud and clay become shale.

Non-clastic sedimentary rocks include those produced by chemical precipitation and by organic activity. Limestones, travertine, rock gypsum, and coal are some of the sedimentary rocks classified as non-clastics.

 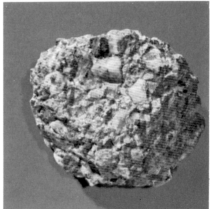

Conglomerate The waterworn pebbles of the original gravel can easily be seen in this specimen, recovered from the Saar region of Germany. Conglomerates will show a color contrast between pebbles and matrix material that varies in intensity.

Breccia This sedimentary rock differs from conglomerate in that the pebbles are angular rather than rounded. The shape of the pebbles indicate that they have not been transported far from their place of origin. The specimen is from Point of Rocks, Maryland.

Sandstone   Consisting mainly of quartz grains cemented together, sandstone is the result of the effects of wind, water and ice on older rock. Strata of the original sand beds can be seen in this specimen from Yorkshire, England. This rock is sometimes called "Millstone Grit" because of its use as grinding stones in mills.

Sandstone (fossiliferous)   The fossils embedded in this sandstone sample are the well-known Silurian trilobite, *Dalmanites*. Beds of sandstone will vary considerably in thickness. The specimen is a relatively fine-grained sandstone from Moravia, Czechoslovakia.

Shale   The fine-grained shales are the result of clays that have hardened into rock. This example is altered very little from the original clay. It is, in fact, termed "fire clay" because of its economic use in making brick, tile, and pottery. The specimen is from Golden, Colorado.

Shale (fossiliferous)   Black and dark gray shales, like this example, typically contain a high content of organic matter within the original shale constituents of clay or mud. This specimen from Newport, Rhode Island, contains the impression of a Coal Age fern.

Limestone   The sugary texture in this sample is characteristic of the majority of limestones. Much "marble" used for decorative building purposes is simply limestone similar to this specimen taken from Bavaria, Germany, that has been polished. Limestone is also widely used in the manufacture of Portland cement.

Limestone (fossiliferous)   This individual specimen illustrates a number of limestone aspects, which vary considerably in texture, cleavage and color. The example, from Coryell County, Texas, contains the fossils of Cretaceous snails.

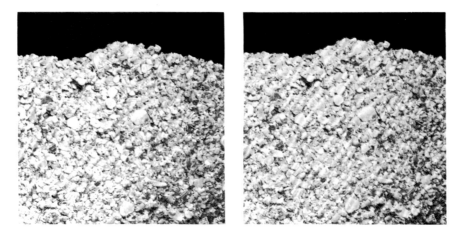

Coquina   This rock is a variety of limestone that consists almost entirely of animal remains. From St. Augustine, Florida, this example contains fossils of marine clams and snails. Other coquinas may contain the remains of brachiopods, crinoids, foraminifera, and other fossils.

Oolitic limestone   The term "oolitic" is derived from the Greek meaning egg and stone, and refers to the small round grains resembling fish eggs in the rock. The formation is normally the result of concentric layers of lime being deposited around a grain of sand or fragment of shell. This specimen from Bromide, Oklahoma, has been secondarily silicified.

Travertine   This rock is a variety of limestone formed by the deposition of calcium carbonate dissolved in water. Cave deposits, such as this specimen from Brazil, Indiana, are the most common occurrences of travertine.

Tufa   The name of this form of limestone is applied to a porous variety of travertine. Tufa is a lightweight rock formed from the deposits of springs and streams. It is also known as "sinter." The specimen is from New York State.

Rock gypsum   The vast beds of the mineral gypsum are associated with and generally described as sedimentary rocks. These beds have been left by the evaporation of inland seas that have been cut off from the ocean basins by geological changes. Iron stains may give rock gypsum a yellow or red hue. This specimen is from Chichagof Island, Alaska.

Coal   The product of decayed vegetable matter, coal is classified according to the amount of remaining water and volatile matter. This specimen is anthracite coal, the highest grade with the lowest remaining water and volatile content. It has a high luster, and unlike bituminous coal is hard and relatively clean. It is from Crested Butte Mine, Colorado.

METAMORPHIC ROCKS

Metamorphic rocks were originally igneous or sedimentary rocks that were altered from their original texture and composition by the forces of heat, pressure and chemical action. Such metamorphism frequently involves the recrystallization of the original parent rock into a different mineral composition.

Metamorphic rocks are often divided into meta-sedimentary and meta-igneous rocks, but in the case of severe metamorphism it is impossible to determine unquestionably the nature of the parent rock. Mildly metamorphosed sedimentary rocks form a definite series: conglomerates typically become gneiss or certain varieties of schist; sandstone forms quartzite; shale becomes slate or phyllite; and limestone changes to marble. Igneous rocks, through the process of metamorphism, become gneiss, schist, phyllite or serpentine.

The continuing cycle and force of geological processes can also cause rocks to undergo more than one metamorphism, so that the resulting rock will represent a further alteration of a previously metamorphosed rock.

Slate This metamorphic rock is characterized by the ease in which it can be split into thin sheets. The cleavage, primarily the result of the metamorphic process, is often at an angle to the original bedding plane of the parent shale, as in this sample from Newfoundland. The strata of the shale can be seen across the face of the slaty cleavage.

Phyllite The further metamorphism of slate often produces phyllite. Its glossy luster is due to the secondarily-produced muscovite mica. Coarse-grained phyllites grade into mica schist. Other phyllites are produced by the metamorphism of felsite. This specimen is from Cornerbrook, Newfoundland.

Mica schist   As its name suggests, mica schist is composed largely of mica and quartz. Usually both muscovite and biotite are present in the rock. Schist is produced by fairly severe metamorphism of sedimentary rocks. This example is from New York City.

Garnet mica schist   Certain mica schists contain relatively large, well-formed crystals of secondary minerals, especially kyanite, staurolite and garnets. The large garnet (diameter: 2 cm) in this specimen from Fort Wrangell, Alaska, displays distinct polyhedral crystal form.

Hornblende schist   This metamorphic rock, in contrast to mica schist, is usually derived from igneous rather than sedimentary parent rock. Besides hornblende, other component minerals are quartz, feldspar, and mica, but these are often too small to be detected megascopically. This specimen is from New York City.

Chlorite schist　　This rock is produced by the fairly severe metamorphism of gabbro or basalt. Chlorite schist and related chlorite-bearing metamorphic rocks are frequently called "greenstones." This example was found at Chester, Massachusetts.

Serpentine　　The name serpentine is given to both a mineral and the metamorphic rock that is predominantly composed of that mineral. Because of its color and luster when polished, the rock has been used for decorative purposes, and some weathered serpentines have proved to be valuable ores of iron, nickel, or chromium. This example is from New York State.

Gneiss　　The term "gneiss" refers to the texture of this metamorphic rock, which is characterized by roughly developed, imperfect foliation resulting from the parallel arrangement of the constituent minerals. Rocks showing gneissic texture may vary widely in chemical composition and origin. This example from Keene, New Hampshire, is composed largely of hornblende, biotite and garnet.

Marble   This rock is derived from the metamorphism of limestone or dolomite. The sugary texture is typical as in this specimen from the Santa Maria Mountains of California. Because of its high luster when polished, marble has a widespread use in art and architecture.

Quartzite   The metamorphic rock, quartzite, differs from the parent sandstone in that the cement between grains is harder than the grains themselves. Therefore, quartzite will break across the quartz grains. Some quartzites contain secondary minerals as the result of metamorphism, such as the kyanite in this specimen taken from South Carolina.

Hornfels   This metamorphic rock is formed when the intrusion of an igneous mass into shale or slate "bakes" the parent rock into a hard aphanitic rock resembling basalt. Its color is usually dark and often spotted or banded. This example is from the Hartz Mountains of Germany.

MINERALS

Minerals, the basic components of rocks, can either be a single element, like gold, or a compound, the chemical combination of different elements.

A mineral has definite physical characteristics, such as general appearance, hardness, specific gravity and crystal form, that provide the keys to proper identification. Classifying minerals after they have been identified leads to an understanding of the origin, history and relationships of the members of the mineral kingdom.

The most common system of classification was developed by the American mineralogist, James Dana. The Dana system, the order that is generally followed in this chapter, is based on the chemical properties of minerals. All of the important chemical groups are included: the native elements, the sulfides, oxides, halides, carbonates, borates, phosphates, sulfates and the silicates. The chemical composition (formula) follows the caption for each mineral. In addition to the chemical formula within the brackets is the crystal group to which the mineral belongs. Models of the six crystal systems are illustrated and explained on pages 62 and 63 to provide both definition and the opportunity for comparison with the mineral specimen.

The large, well-formed minerals illustrated in this chapter occur under conditions that are not typical of rocks in general. They are the result of various geological processes: very slow cooling of igneous magma; prolonged metamorphic stress that leads to recrystallization of the parent rock; deposition by ground water of mineral substances within rock cavities; or weathering and oxidation of existing mineral specimens converting them to other minerals. The specimens appearing here, however, are typical and include the most common and important minerals, plus a few that are notable for striking color or crystal form.

The minerals shown at the left are (from the top): sulfur, stichtite in serpentine, malachite and marcasite (bottom left).

Native gold   Gold is found in various forms. As an element, it occurs mainly as minute specks scattered through quartz veins. Larger clusters have a leaf-like appearance, which becomes rounded into nuggets when carried by streams. These specimens are from the mining district at Breckenridge, Colorado. [Au; Cubic crystals]

Native silver   The wiry twisted structure shown by this sample from Keweenaw Point, Michigan, is a typical occurrence of native silver. Specimens with similar appearance sometimes prove to be mixtures of native silver and native copper and are known as "half-breed." [Ag; Cubic crystals]

Native copper   This element is usually found in volcanic rocks and in veins. Native copper is abundant enough to be classed as an ore at the source of this sample, LaPaz, Bolivia. Pre-Colombian Indians often used native copper to fashion implements and ornaments. Northern Michigan is a rich source of copper in the United States. [Cu; Cubic crystals]

Sulfur   Sicily is noted as an important source for well-developed crystals of native sulfur, like the example illustrated here (on aragonite). Sulfur is produced by the cooling of igneous gasses and also by the alteration of gypsum. It is widely used in industry (matches, gunpowder, vulcanized rubber) and in agriculture as a fertilizer. [S; Orthorhombic crystals]

Graphite   This shiny gray mineral is one of two varieties of native carbon; the other is diamond. The familiar "lead" in pencils is actually graphite, which has numerous other economic uses. This specimen is from Ceylon. [C; Hexagonal crystals]

Chalcocite   This mineral is the most important ore of copper, although it may be the least colorful. Chalcocite is typically found in veins along with bornite, chalcopyrite, enargite, and other sulfides. The specimen is from England. [Cu_2S; Orthorhombic crystals]

Bornite   A sulfide of copper and iron, bornite is generally found in veins or in igneous rocks. The older name of "Peacock Copper" well describes the aspect of this sample from Utah. The gold-like flakes are chalcopyrite. In some localities bornite is abundant enough to be classed as an ore. [Cu_5FeS_4; Cubic crystals]

Galena   The chief source of lead, galena is usually found in either veins or rock beds. Galena is also a valuable silver ore. Its typical cubic crystals are set off in this example by leaf-like marcasite. This specimen is from Galena, Illinois, a town that derived its name from the rich deposits of the mineral. [PbS; Cubic crystals]

Sphalerite   This brittle mineral is the chief ore of zinc. The texture and color of sphalerite can vary considerably, and is often found in association with galena, chalcopyrite, barite, fluorite, etc. This specimen is from Kokomo, Colorado. [ZnS; Cubic crystals]

Chalcopyrite   The most common and widespread of copper minerals, chalcopyrite is often confused with pyrite. This brittle primary mineral is also the source from which many secondary copper minerals are derived. This example is from Picher, Oklahoma. [$CuFeS_2$; Tetragonal crystals]

Pyrrhotite   This mineral is frequently found mixed with pentlandite in sufficient quantity to serve as a valuable nickel ore. Another name for pyrrhotite is "magnetic pyrites," because of the variable magnetism in some examples. This specimen is from Chihuahua, Mexico. [$Fe_{1-x}S$; Hexagonal crystals]

Cinnabar   This specimen from New Almaden, California shows the characteristic deep red color of cinnabar. The color may vary, however, from brown to dull gray. Cinnabar is the chief ore of mercury. It is usually found near hot springs and volcanic areas. [HgS; Hexagonal crystals]

Stibnite   This specimen from Romania displays especially striking crystals. Stibnite is the chief ore of antimony, which is used extensively in metallurgy and in storage batteries. It is typically found in quartz veins, associated with galena, barite, cinnabar, and other minerals. [Sb_2S_3; Orthorhombic crystals]

Pyrite   This mineral occurs in widely different forms—massive, granular, and crystalline. This specimen from Illinois shows well-formed crystals. When dispersed in quartz veins, pyrite is often mistaken for gold and has earned the epithet "Fool's Gold." [FeS_2; Cubic crystals]

Cobaltite   The silvery white mineral, cobaltite, in this example is associated with quartz and actinolite. As its name suggests, it is an ore of cobalt, which is widely used in metallurgy. It is often found in association with nickel minerals. This specimen is from Espanola, Ontario, a major cobalt-producing area. [$CoAsS$; Cubic crystals]

Marcasite   This mineral has the same chemical composition as pyrite. Marcasite, however, forms under lower temperatures and from more acidic magma than pyrite and has a different crystal system. Like pyrite, it occurs in varied aspects. Marcasite is sometimes called "white iron pyrites." The specimen is from Galena, Illinois. [FeS_2; Orthorhombic crystals]

Arsenopyrite   A major source of metallic arsenic and arsenic compounds, arsenopyrite is typically found with tin and tungsten ores and in pegmatites. In rare cases, it contains economic impurities of gold or silver. Its occurrence may be either massive or as crystals. This specimen is from Hohenstein, Germany. [$FeAsS$; Monoclinic crystals]

Enargite   In this example, the black mineral, enargite, is shown growing on quartz crystals. Enargite is important both as an ore of copper and as a source of arsenic oxide. It is normally composed of copper, antimony and arsenic. This specimen is from Red Mountain in San Juan County, Colorado. [Cu_3AsS_4; Orthorhombic crystals]

Cuprite   An important ore of copper, cuprite is a secondary mineral formed by the oxidation of other copper minerals. Its color can vary from ruby red to almost black. Cuprite may be found as crystal, granular or massive occurrences. This specimen is from Hanover Mine, Fierro, New Mexico. [Cu_2O; Cubic crystals]

Corundum   One of the hardest substances in nature, corundum has a rating of 9 on the Mohs hardness scale. A primary aluminum mineral, it is widely used as an abrasive. Both the ruby and the sapphire are varieties of corundum (see *Gems*). These typical prisms are from Macon County, North Carolina. [Al_2O_3; Hexagonal crystals]

Zincite   Despite its name, this mineral is not the principle ore of zinc. The color of zincite can vary from dark red to orange yellow. This specimen is from Franklin Furnace, New Jersey, a locality famous for its abundance of zincite deposits and the occurrence of rare and unusual minerals. [ZnO; Hexagonal crystals]

Hematite   This mineral is extremely variable as to texture and form; its color can range from dull earthy red to near-black. Hematite is the most important ore of iron. It is the chief mineral in the Lake Superior iron ranges. This specimen is from Cumberland, England. [Fe_2O_3; Hexagonal crystals]

Rutile   This mineral, consisting of titanium dioxide, occurs widely (titanium is one of the ten most abundant elements in the earth's crust), but is rarely found in abundance in one location. This specimen from Sudbury, Pennsylvania, shows the typical near-black color of rutile. The crystal form is known as an "elbow twin." [TiO_2; Tetragonal crystals]

Pyrolusite   An important ore of manganese, pyrolusite often occurs in association with psilomelane. Specimens vary in texture and color. It is important as a coloring agent in printing, pottery, bricks and paint. This specimen is from Bohemia, Czechoslovakia. [MnO_2; Tetragonal crystals]

Cassiterite   This mineral is the only important ore of tin and is frequently called "tin-stone." It is usually found in pegmatite and granite rocks. A fibrous variety is called "wood tin." This specimen is from Saxony, Germany. [SnO_2; Tetragonal crystals]

Bauxite   A mineral secondarily produced by the weathering of aluminum-bearing rock, bauxite is the chief ore of aluminum. This specimen from Tennessee exhibits a typical texture of spherical concretions within an amorphous background, known as *pisolitic* texture. [$Al_2O_3 \cdot 2H_2O$; *Amorphous* crystals]

Psilomelane   The composition of psilomelane often varies. Manganese atoms are frequently replaced by barium, cobalt, copper, or lead, and even the exact formula is in doubt. Psilomelane, an important source of manganese, occurs as a secondary mineral. This example from Michigan has a *botryoidal* (grape-cluster) shape. [$BaMn_1O_{18} \cdot 2H_2O$; Orthorhombic crystals]

Limonite   This specimen from Pennsylvania is typical of the earthy texture and color of limonite, a hydrated oxide of iron. An alteration product of other iron ores and minerals, limonite is an important source of iron. A crystalline variety of the mineral is called goethite. [$FeO(OH) \cdot nH_2O$; Orthorhombic crystals]

Magnetite   This important magnetic iron ore combines iron in both ferric and ferrous forms; the latter frequently being replaced in part by manganese, magnesium, or zinc. When occurring as a natural magnet it is known as "lodestone." This specimen is from Essex County, New York. [Fe_3O_4; Cubic crystals]

Chromite   This mineral is the principal source of chromium, used to make chrome steel. Chromite may also contain magnesium, aluminum and iron. Chromite occurs chiefly in basic igneous rocks and is also associated with serpentine. This example is from the Philippine Islands. [$FeCr_2O_4$; Cubic crystals]

Fluorite   The typical cubic crystals are "frosted" with quartz in this specimen. Fluorite, one of the most beautiful minerals, occurs in many different colors. It is used extensively as a flux in steel-making. This specimen is from Cumberland, England, a locality famous for excellent fluorite crystals. [CaF_2; Cubic crystals]

Fluorite   This somewhat paler specimen is also from Cumberland, England, and shows the variation that can occur in fluorite examples. Fluorite has excellent crystal formation, which can be seen in this close-up photo of a detail of the mineral. Fluorite is also used in the making of opalescent glass and enamel cooking utensils. [CaF_2; Cubic crystals]

Calcite   Calcite occurs in a wide variety of crystal forms, colors, and aspects. This specimen from Chihuahua, Mexico, shows the typical rhombohedral cleavage characteristic of calcite. This form is the variety known as "Iceland spar," remarkable for its double refraction of light. [$CaCO_3$; Hexagonal crystals]

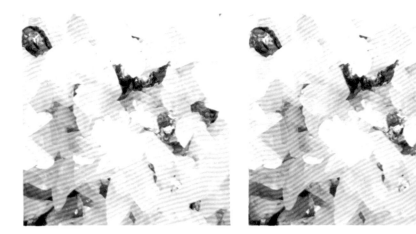

Calcite   The mineral calcite is the essential constituent of limestone, where it occurs in great masses. The striking crystal forms are clearly visible in the close-up of this specimen from Cumberland, England. The gold metallic deposits interspersed among the calcite are pyrite. [CaCO$_3$; Hexagonal crystals]

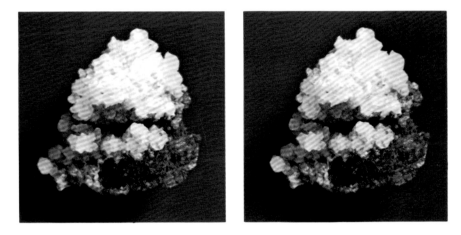

Pink Calcite   This pink specimen from Chihuahua, Mexico, illustrates one of the variety of colors in which calcite can occur. The color variations of calcite are caused by impurities in the mineral. Calcite, with its varying shapes and colors, is one of the most widespread of all minerals. [CaCO$_3$; Hexagonal crystals]

Siderite   This mineral is an occasional source of iron and frequently contains important impurities of manganese. It is often found in association with rhodochrosite and magnesite. This specimen is from Idaho Springs, Colorado.[FeCO$_3$; Hexagonal crystals]

Rhodochrosite This specimen from Butte, Montana, shows the pink color typical of pure rhodochrosite. The mineral occurs mainly in veins cutting across other ore bodies. Rhodochrosite is a minor ore of manganese. [$MnCO_3$; Hexagonal crystals]

Smithsonite The bumpy texture shown in this example is a typical aspect of smithsonite. The mineral also exhibits a considerable color variety. Smithsonite is a minor ore of zinc. This example is from Ophir, Utah. [$ZnCO_3$; Hexagonal crystals]

Aragonite A less common form of calcium carbonate, aragonite has the same chemical composition as calcite but is a less stable mineral. Aragonite gradually turns into calcite, especially at high temperatures. This specimen from Utah shows striking radiated crystallization. [$CaCO_3$; Orthorhombic crystals]

Aragonite   This specimen from Styria, Austria is typical of aragonite that has been deposited from hot ground water or lava flows. It is a branching growth called "flos-ferri" (flowers of iron) and is formed in caves and mines. [$CaCO_3$; Orthorhombic crystals]

Cerussite   In either crystal form or masses, cerussite occurs as a secondary mineral produced by the weathering of lead ores. Cerussite often contains values of silver. This specimen is from the New Stockton Mine near Salt Lake City, Utah. [$PbCO_3$; Orthorhombic crystals]

Dolomite   Huge masses of dolomite occur as rock formations, and typically have been formed by the chemical alteration of limestone. Dolomite is a source for magnesium compounds and carbon dioxide. Well-formed crystals, such as these from Cumberland, England, are less common than massive forms [$CaMg(CO_3)_2$; Hexagonal crystals]

Malachite   The attractive green mineral, malachite, occurs in different forms. The most common form is *botryoidal* (grape-cluster), as illustrated by this specimen from the Ural Mountains. Malachite is used as an ornamental stone, especially in Russia. [$Cu_2CO_3(OH)_2$; Monoclinic crystals]

Malachite   This specimen from Utah shows a different but still important form of malachite. An important ore of copper, malachite is frequently found with other copper-bearing minerals and is closely associated with azurite. [$Cu_2CO_3(OH)_2$; Monoclinic crystals]

Azurite   A secondary mineral found in oxidation zones of copper ore deposits, azurite alters easily into malachite. Its brilliant color can vary from light azure to deep blue. Azurite, unlike malachite, can also be found in well-formed crystals. This example is from Bisbee, Arizona. [$Cu_3(OH)_2(CO_3)_2$; Monoclinic crystals]

Kernite The large white crystals of the specimen are typical occurrences of this recently discovered mineral (1926). Kernite is an important source of borax. The specimen is from Kern County, California, the area for which the mineral is named and a noted locality for borate minerals. [$Na_2B_4O_7 \cdot 4H_2O$; Monoclinic crystals]

Borax The mineral, borax, is rather rare in its natural state (as it is shown here). Most borax, used widely in washing powders and to a lesser degree in medicines, is made artifically from kernite or other borates. This specimen is from Boron, California. [$Na_2B_4O_7 \cdot 10H_2O$; Monoclinic crystals]

Colemanite First found in Death Valley, California, colemanite was the major source of borax until kernite was discovered. It can occur in either massive deposits or in well-formed crystals as in this specimen. This example is from Calico, California. [$Ca_2B_6O_{11} \cdot 5H_2O$; Monoclinic crystals]

Barite   This mineral, a source of barium, is often found in association with celestite, as well as with lead, copper and silver ores. Because of its high density, barite is sometimes called "heavy spar." There is considerable variation in the color form of barite occurrences. This specimen is from Dugway, Utah. [$BaSO_4$; Orthorhombic crystals]

Celestite   A mineral that closely resembles barite, celestite is an important source of strontium compounds. It usually occurs in association with limestone, and may contain a blue tint. This white crystal spray from Clay Center, Ohio, is a typical specimen, although considerable variety of form and color in celestite is known. [$SrSO_4$, Orthorhombic crystals]

Gypsum   The common and commercially important mineral, gypsum, usually occurs in massive beds. Gypsum may occur in different aspects and crystal forms. When found in thick beds, gypsum is frequently considered a rock type (see *ROCKS*, p. 16). Gypsum is the basic source of plaster of Paris. This specimen is from New Mexico. [$CaSO_4 \cdot 2H_2O$; Monoclinic crystals]

Crocoite   A rare but especially beautiful mineral, crocoite is formed by the action of chromic acid on lead minerals. It is a minor ore of chromium, but has little commercial importance. This specimen from Dundas, Tasmania, shows the red crocoite crystals against a background made up of the mineral goethite. [$PbCrO_4$; Monoclinic crystals]

Erythrite   This unusually fine specimen of erythrite is from Bou Azzer, Morocco. Erythrite is produced by the oxidation of cobalt minerals, and is frequently called "cobalt bloom." The red mineral is not abundant enough to be useful as an ore, but it is a good indicator of the presence of other cobalt minerals. [$Co_3As_2O_8 \cdot 8\,H_2O$; Monoclinic crystals]

Mimetite   A relatively uncommon mineral, mimetite often shows striking radial crystals, as in this example from South West Africa. Mimetite is a secondary mineral normally found in oxided zones of lead ore deposits. It is quite similar to pyromorphite, and is usually found in association with it. [$Pb_5Cl(AsO_4)_3$; Hexagonal crystals]

Apatite   An abundant mineral, apatite is a source of phosphorous. In some areas, phosphate deposits consisting mainly of apatite are extensive and have economic value as constituents of fertilizer. This specimen from Renfrew, Ontario, shows a typical prismatic crystal of apatite in calcite. [$Ca_5(F, Cl)(PO_4)_3$; Hexagonal crystals]

Apatite   This rare example of a transparent purple form of apatite is from Auburn, Maine. The crystals are set in cookeite, a lithium-aluminum silicate related to lepidolite. The mineral is occasionally used in jewelry but is too soft to make a satisfactory gemstone. [$Ca_5(F, Cl)(PO_4)_3$; Hexagonal crystals]

Autunite   This attractive yellow-green mineral is relatively uncommon, and is a result of the oxidation of uranium ores. It is often associated with uraninite. This example from Mount Spokane, Washington, is quite radioactive. [$Ca(UO_2)_2(PO_4)_2 \cdot 10\text{-}12H_2O$; Tetragonal crystals]

Novacekite   Like autunite, novacekite is a secondary mineral produced by the oxidation of uranium minerals. It shows the bright yellow color characteristic of many uranium-bearing minerals. This specimen is from Chihuahua, Mexico. [$Mg(UO_2)_2(AsO_4)_2 \cdot 8\text{-}10H_2O$; Tetragonal crystals]

Carnotite   This mineral was formerly mined for its contents of vanadium and radium. The atomic age promoted it into an important source of uranium. It typically occurs as streaks or grains in sandstone, as shown in this specimen from Edgemont, South Dakota. [$K_2(UO_2)_2V_2O_8 \cdot 3\,H_2O$; Orthorhombic crystals]

Wolframite   This specimen from Colorado represents huebnerite, the manganese end of the Fe-Mn spectrum. It is typically found in pegmatites and veins. Wolframite is the chief source of tungsten. [$(Fe, Mn)WO_4$; Monoclinic crystals]

Scheelite   A widespread mineral, scheelite occurs both in pegmatites and veins and as a contact metamorphic mineral. Its color ranges from white through shades of yellow, red, green and brown. Scheelite is an important ore of tungsten in the United States. [$CaWO_4$; Tetragonal crystals]

Olivine   This specimen from Germany represents chrysolite, the high-magnesium variety of olivine. A blend of magnesium and iron silicates, olivine is an essential constituent of basalt, gabbro, and peridotite. A transparent variety, called *peridot*, is used as a gemstone. [$(Mg, Fe)_2 SiO_4$; Orthorhombic crystals]

Kyanite   The name of this mineral is derived from the Greek word for blue. Kyanite is found only in metamorphic rocks, often associated with garnets. This specimen from Sugar Loaf Mountain, North Carolina, displays typical blade-like crystals against a quartz matrix. [Al_2SiO_5; Triclinic crystals]

Sphene Also known as titanite, sphene is a minor ore of titanium, and rare clear crystals are sometimes fashioned into gems. Sphene is a common accessory mineral in both igneous and metamorphic rocks. This example is from Eganville, Ontario. [$CaTiSiO_4$; Monoclinic crystals]

Epidote Like kyanite, this green mineral is typically produced by metamorphism. Exceptionally fine crystals of epidote are sometimes used as gemstones. This specimen from North Carolina shows the slender crystals of epidote on albite. [$Ca_2(Al, Fe)_3 (SiO_4)_3 (OH)$; Monoclinic crystals]

Chrysocolla A minor ore of copper, chrysocolla also has been used for ornamental purposes and as a gemstone. It is a secondary mineral usually blue or green, that results from the oxidation of other copper compounds. This specimen is from Mapimi, Mexico. [$CuSiO_3 \cdot 2H_2O$; Amorphous crystals]

Beryl   This attractive mineral is the primary source of the rare element beryllium. It occurs both in pegmatites and in metamorphic rocks. The gems aquamarine and emerald are varieties of beryl (see *GEMS*). This example is from Minas Geraes, Brazil. [$Be_3Al_2Si_6O_{18}$; Hexagonal crystals]

Diopside   This mineral, one of the highly variable pyroxene minerals, is a calcium-magnesium-silicate with short prismatic crystals. Diopside is often similar to and closely associated with tremolite. This specimen is from Nordmark, Sweden. [$CaMgSi_2O_6$; Monoclinic crystals]

Augite   The most common of the pyroxene minerals, augite is a blend of aluminum, iron, magnesium, and calcium silicates. It typically occurs in igneous rocks, especially in basaltic lavas. This example of augite is from Russell, New York. [$Ca(Mg,Fe,Al)(Al,Si)_2O_6$; Monoclinic crystals]

Tremolite   One of the most common of the amphibole group of minerals is tremolite. It occurs chiefly in impure crystalline limestones and dolomites, in contact metamorphic zones and in some schists. This example of tremolite, in dolomite, is from Campolungo, Switzerland. [$Ca_2Mg_5Si_8O_{22}(OH)_2$; Monoclinic crystals]

Actinolite   Another amphibole mineral, actinolite differs chemically from tremolite only in that iron has replaced some of the magnesium. Actinolite normally has a darker green color than tremolite. This specimen is from Mineral Hill, Pennsylvania. [$Ca_2(Mg,Fe)_5Si_8O_{22}(OH)_2$; Monoclinic crystals]

Hornblende   Common hornblende, an amphibole mineral, is a mixture of sodium, calcium, iron, and magnesium silicates. It also contains aluminum and occurs in both igneous and metamorphic rocks. Because of its chemical complexity, a formula is not given. This specimen is from Chester, Massachusetts. [Monoclinic crystals]

Crocidolite   This mineral is a fibrous form of the amphibole mineral riebeckite. Crocidolite is, commercially important as "blue asbestos." (Asbestos is a fibrous texture designation.) This specimen in association with hematite is from the Trough Lake area on the Quebec/Labrador border. [$H_2Na_2Fe_3Fe_2Si_8O_{24}$; Monoclinic crystals]

Rhodonite   Occurrences of rhodonite are typically massive, and well-formed crystals such as these from Broken Hill, New South Wales, are rare. Exceptionally good specimens are sometimes made into gemstones. The crystals here are embedded in galena. [$MnSiO_3$; Triclinic crystals]

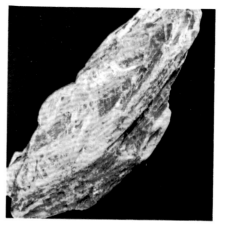

Talc   The softest mineral, talc is typically an alteration product of pyroxene or amphibole minerals. Talc has numerous commercial uses, ranging from industrial products to cosmetics. This specimen is from Minas Geraes, Brazil. [$Mg_3Si_4O_{10}(OH)_2$; Monoclinic crystals]

Muscovite   Sometimes called "white mica," muscovite occurs typically in granite, syenite, pegmatite and in mica schist. Originally used as a substitute for glass, it is used widely today for electrical and heat insulation. This specimen is from Batchellerville, New York. [$KAl_3Si_3O_{10}(OH)_2$; Monoclinic crystals]

Biotite   This specimen from Guatemala shows the typical slate-like cleavage characteristic of biotite. Sometimes called "iron mica," it has a variable composition and occurs widely in granite, syenite, diorite, gneiss, and schist. Biotite has little commercial importance. [$K(Mg, Fe)_3AlSi_3O_{10}(OH)_2$; Monoclinic crystals]

Lepidolite   An important source of lithium compounds, lepidolite commonly occurs as small specks within pegmatites, granite, or as in this large specimen from Rozna, Moravia, on gneiss. Its nature as mica can be seen when lepidolite is present as a band around muscovite, as in the example on the right from Haddam Neck, Connecticut. [$K_2Li_3Al_4Si_7O_{21}(OH_1F)_3$; Monoclinic crystals]

Chlorite   Like the pyroxene and amphibole minerals, chlorite is a blend of several end-members and varies widely in composition. It is the dominant mineral in chlorite schist (see *ROCKS*, p. 19). This specimen, from Brewster, New York, is on dolomite and is the variety referred to as ripidolite. [$(Mg,Fe)_4Al_2(Si_2Al_2)O_{10}(OH)_8$; Monoclinic crystals]

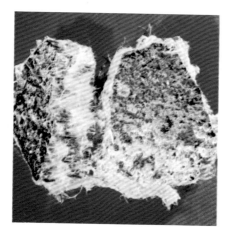
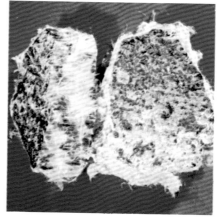

Chrysotile   This mineral is a silky, fibrous variety of serpentine, and is commercially important. Chrysotile is the most abundant source of asbestos. This example is from Asbestos, Quebec. [$(MgOH)_6(Si_2O_6,Si_2O_5) \cdot H_2O$; Monoclinic crystals]

Quartz   The most common of all minerals, quartz is an oxide of silicon. It is extremely variable in crystal form, aspect, and color. This specimen shows typically well-developed crystal forms of the variety of quartz known as *rock crystal*. This specimen is from Guanajuato, Mexico. [SiO_2; Hexagonal crystals]

Smoky quartz   The smoky appearance of some quartz, once believed to be due to iron impurities, is the result of radioactive damage. Radiation from radioactive elements in the surrounding rocks dislocate large numbers of electrons, causing changes in refraction. This fine specimen of smoky quartz is from St. Gotthard, Switzerland. [SiO_2; Hexagonal crystals]

Rutilated quartz   This crystal form of quartz from Minas Geraes, Brazil, contains intergrowths of needle-like rutile crystals. This variety is also referred to as *sagenitic quartz*. Other minerals beside rutile (tourmaline, epidote, etc.) can be enclosed in quartz. [SiO_2; Hexagonal crystals]

Citrine   The yellow color in this variety of quartz is believed to be due to iron impurities. Choice crystals of citrine are often cut for gemstones. Because citrine is sometimes marketed as topaz, it is also referred to as "false topaz." This specimen is from Colorado. [SiO_2; Hexagonal crystals]

Jasper   This term is given to an occurrence of impure, opaque quartz. Jasper is typically red, a result of the inclusion of hematite or possibly limonite. Jasper may, however, be yellow, brown, green, blue, or black. This specimen is from Baden, Germany. [SiO_2; Hexagonal crystals]

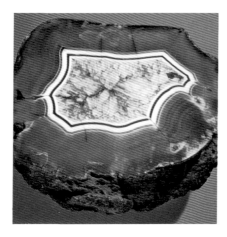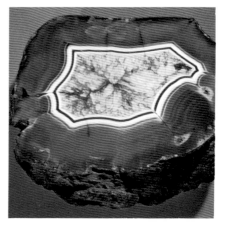

Agate   A variety of *chalcedony*, agate is a form of quartz with different colors arranged in concentric bands. The colors vary in different specimens. This polished specimen from Uruguay has been artificially colored. [SiO_2; Hexagonal crystals]

Albite   A member of the feldspar group of minerals, albite is usually white in color but can vary to gray or light blue. Albite is one of the plagioclase feldspars, a continuous series of six minerals from albite to anorthite. This albite specimen is from Tyrol, Austria. [$NaAlSi_3O_8$; Triclinic crystals]

Labradorite   This variety of the plagioclase feldspars is an almost equal mixture of albite and anorthite. Because of its brilliant iridescent blue, it is often used for ornamental purposes. The name is derived from Labrador, an area where the mineral is especially common and from which this specimen was taken. [Triclinic crystals]

Anorthite   The calcium end-member of the plagioclase feldspars, anorthite is not a common mineral in its pure form. Anorthite occurs in several forms. This anorthite specimen is from Tyrol, Austria. [$CaAl_2Si_2O_8$, Triclinic crystals]

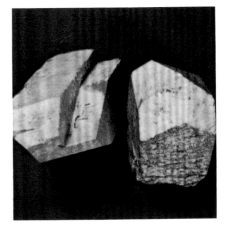

Orthoclase   Another mineral of the feldspar group, orthoclase is found in abundance in granite, syenite, rhyolite, and pegmatite. Orthoclase is a potash feldspar and is used commercially in the making of ceramics, glass, enamels and abrasives. [$KAlSi_3O_8$; Monoclinic crystals]

Microcline   This potash feldspar is abundant in pegmatites, and is typically associated witn orthoclase. Microcline differs from orthoclase in its crystal system, but is difficult to distinguish either visually or chemically. This specimen is from Colorado. [$KAlSi_3O_8$; Triclinic crystals]

Microcline   This specimen is a green variety of microcline known as *amazon stone*, sometimes used as a gemstone. The microcline crystals in this specimen from Crystal Peak, Colorado, are associated with albite (at their base) and smoky quartz. [$KAlSi_3O_8$; Triclinic crystals]

Stilbite   This mineral is the most common of the zeolites, or hydrated calcium-sodium-aluminum silicates. The feathery texture shown by this specimen from Nova Scotia is typical of all zeolite minerals. Stilbite typically occurs in cavities of basic igneous rocks and in veins. [$CaAl_2Si_2O_6 \cdot 6H_2O$; Monoclinic crystals]

GEMS

Gems are minerals by composition, but the definition of which minerals are gems is an arbitrary one, influenced by fashion. There are however, three major criteria for classification as a gem—beauty, durability and rarity.

Even though beauty is a purely subjective quality, determined by fashion and tradition, all three are necessary for classification as a gemstone. Diamonds, for example, occur in color varieties; but even though a yellow-tinged diamond is as durable and rare as a colorless one, the colorless variety is the most prized as a precious gem. Luster—the ability to reflect light —contributes to the precious quality of transparent gems, and the richness of color determines the beauty of the opaque gems.

The distinction is often made between precious stones (diamond, ruby, emerald and sapphire) and semi-precious and ornamental gems. Gems may also be divided into stones that are typically faceted and those that are usually carved.

The names given to gemstones often vary from the mineralogical name. In addition, different gem names are sometimes given to what are merely color variations of a particular gem. The gems in this chapter are identified by the names with which they are most commonly associated.

High-quality specimens of other rocks and minerals not included in this chapter may also qualify as either faceted gemstones or semi-precious decorative pieces. Many of these potentially valuable rocks and minerals appear in the two preceding chapters, and include such diverse specimens as serpentine, marble, dolomite, malachite, azurite, apatite, olivine, rhodonite, jasper, agate, amazon stone, epidote, beryl, quartz and citrine.

The stereograms in this chapter include a cut and uncut specimen of almost all of the gems, to provide a comparison of the raw material in its natural state with the polished and cut gemstones.

The gems shown at the left are (from the top, l. to r.): opal (uncut), sapphire (uncut), topaz, garnet, zircon, golden topaz, sapphire, opal, zircon, and golden topaz (uncut).

Diamond   High-quality diamonds display the three basic characteristics of a gem: they have a sparkling beauty, they are rare, and they are durable (diamond is the hardest naturally-occurring substance). Both specimens are from the Kimberley district of South Africa. The cut stone is four carats; the uncut diamond has been estimated at 12 to 15 carats.

Ruby   The ruby, like the sapphire, is a variety of corundum, the second hardest mineral. The example from Arendal, Norway, of an uncut ruby in syenite is not transparent enough to be of true gem quality. Rubies are characteristically clear red, and high-quality specimens are quite valuable.

Aquamarine   As its name implies, aquamarine (from the Latin for "seawater") is a sparkling blue variety of beryl. Aquamarine is considered a semi-precious gem. The uncut specimens here are from Nertschinsk, Siberia. The cut gem is from Minas Geraes, Brazil.

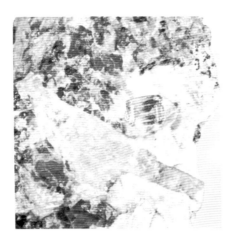
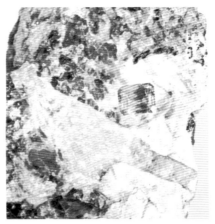

Chrysoberyl   A rare gemstone prized from antiquity, chrysoberyl is usually pale green or yellow. A variety known as *alexandrite* is a deeper emerald green that changes to red under artificial light. The uncut specimen of chrysoberyl is from Haddam, Connecticut; the cut stone is from Brazil.

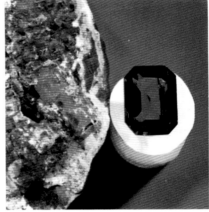

Emerald   A variety of the mineral beryl, emeralds are not especially rare but most have numerous fractures that make them unsuitable for any but the smallest stones. Like most forms of beryl, emeralds typically occur in pegmatites. The uncut emerald here is from Musco, Colombia.

Sapphire   Another variety of corundum, sapphire is a rich blue gem mineral. Some specimens of sapphire (and ruby) have impurities within the hexagonal symmetry, which reflect light in the form of a six-pointed "star." The uncut sapphire specimens are from Kashmir, India.

Topaz   The mineral topaz is almost always found as isolated, well-formed crystals. Yellow topaz is the most valuable, but the gem can also occur colorless, gray, green, blue or red. The uncut crystal specimen and the transparent cut stone ("white topaz") are from the Ural Mountains; the yellow cut stone ("golden topaz") is from Ouro Prieto, Brazil.

Garnet   The most common examples of garnet are red, but the mineral also occurs in a wide variety of colors: white, black, green, yellow, brown and colorless. The most common occurrence of garnets is in mica schists, as in this uncut example from Southbury, Connecticut. The cut stone is from Pegu, India. (See also *Garnet Mica Schist*, p. 18.)

Zircon   This gem is common as an accessory mineral in igneous rocks, typically occurring as well-formed crystals of various coloring. Besides its use as a gemstone, zircon has commercial value as a source of zirconium compounds. The zircon crystal in matrix here is from the Ural Mountains.

Tourmaline   Another mineral of variable composition, tourmaline may be black, brown, blue, green, red, pink, or colorless, and sometimes displays as many as four or five distinct hues in a single (uncut) crystal. The uncut crystals are from Mesa Grande, Colorado, and the larger pink specimen rimmed in green (nicknamed "watermelon") is from Maine.

Spinel   This gemstone is highly variable in both composition and color. Spinel is frequently collected from stream gravels, after it has been eroded from crystalline limestones or schists. It is often found in association with gem varieties of corundum. The gravel specimens shown here are from Ceylon.

Jade   The designation "jade" has been given to two distinct minerals: *jadeite*, related to pyroxene; and *nephrite*, part of the amphibole group of minerals. Jade has been favored for jewelry and sculptured art in the Orient as well as in ancient Mexico. The specimen of jadeite shown here is from Petaluma, California.

Moonstone   The name "moonstone" is given to both an opalescent variety of orthoclase (as illustrated by this specimen) and to albite with intergrown orthoclase which also creates an opalescent effect. The uncut specimen of moonstone is from Magaung, Burma; the cut gems are from Kandy, Ceylon.

Lapis lazuli   The gemstone lapis lazuli is a variety of the mineral lazurite, a sodium-aluminum silicate, with some admixture of sulfur. Its color can vary from the rich azure blue of this example to a greenish-blue. The cut stone and the smaller uncut gem are from Bolivia. The larger uncut stone is from Afghanistan.

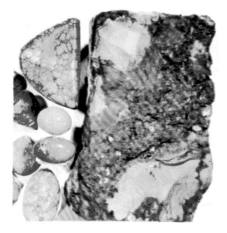
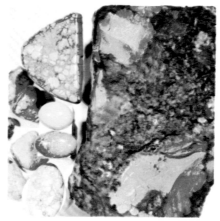

Turquoise   The highest quality specimens of turquoise are sky blue, but green and mottled blue-green are much more common. Turquoise is a popular gemstone in India and among the American Indians of the Southwest. The large uncut specimen is from New Mexico; the cut gemstones show varying aspects of turquoise.

Opal   This is one mineral that does not occur in crystals. It is believed to be hardened gelatinous silica, and it has a high water content. The most prized specimens show a play of colors, known as *fire,* when slowly turned. The two specimens are from Australia.

 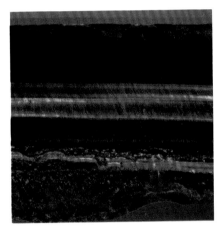

Tiger's eye   This fibrous gem material is basically a silica containing inclusions arranged in parallel streaks of yellow and brown. When slowly turned, the streaks give the gem a play of colors termed *chatoyancy*. This specimen is from Griqualand, South West Africa, the source of nearly all gem-quality tiger's eye.

Amethyst   The color in this variety of quartz can vary from pale violet to a deep purple, and is thought to be the result of manganese impurities. Naturally-occurring crystals of amethyst are seldom large, and most cut stones are correspondingly small. This crystal group here is from Guanajuato, Mexico.

LUNAR ROCKS

The large features of the lunar surface have been known and mapped for over 100 years. Many studies have made it apparent that the prominent lunar craters and huge plains (the "maria" or "seas") are the result of past impacts and explosions of large meteorite bodies, modified by the outpourings of lava. Other features, such as the lunar mountain chains and "rills" are less well understood.

It has long been believed that the moon is composed of a thick outer layer of a rock of basaltic composition, which has about the right mean density and gray color and only a small, if any, central core. The moon's low efficiency of light reflection (*albedo*) has been attributed to the impacts of millions of micrometeorites over billions of years so that the surface is pocked with small pits that provide light traps, reducing the amount of sunlight that is reflected.

The information gathered by Surveyor V has revealed some major irregularities in composition—the element titanium is 20 to 25 times higher in the lunar surface than in any terrestrial basalt, and the element sodium is eight to 10 times lower. Preliminary analyses of some of the Apollo 11 samples give the same results. Early mineralogical examination shows that much of the excess titanium is due to an unusual amount of the mineral *ilmenite*, which is found in terrestrial basalts, but only in very small quantities. The lunar samples also show the presence of large amounts of plagioclase with a higher calcium content and lower sodium content than in terrestrial basalts. While it appears that the lunar rocks are similar to basalt, they are not the normal type that was predicted. From close-up photographs, like the following stereograms, it is clear that the surface rocks are not entirely homogeneous, and variations in composition will be found as further analyses are made.

The stereo photographs shown here reveal that the surface is indeed peppered with micrometeorite impact pits. The Earth does not receive these small impacts because its thick atmosphere burns and destroys all but the larger meteorite bodies. The airless lunar surface permits full impact of all meteorite sizes, down to the smallest specks. Besides the pitting action of these micrometeorites (which impact at an average velocity of 17 kilometers per second) they act as an erosional agent chipping and rounding the surface rocks over eons of time.

The close-up stereograms of lunar rocks were provided through the courtesy of the National Aeronautics and Space Administration (NASA), and were photographed on the surface of the moon by the Apollo 11 astronauts.

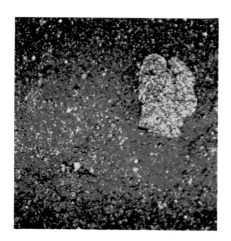
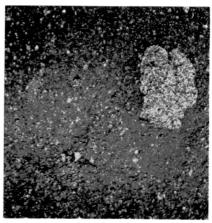

Lunar Rocks   This stereogram shows the heterogeneous nature of lunar surface rocks. The dark gray matrix rock contains many small clusters of white minerals and one large inclusion (.75 inch by 1.2 inches) of a different rock type. The inclusion may consist mostly of plagioclase. Over the entire area are hundreds of tiny pits with shiny glaze-like surfaces, possibly the impact marks of micrometeorites.

Lunar Rocks The fairly homogeneous rock in this stereogram shows some color variation, probably due to lighting effects. Many small spherical particles as well as irregular mineral grains are protruding from the fine-grained, gray rock matrix. This texture and relief may be due to micrometeorite impacts. Some of the mineral grains glitter brightly indicating well-formed, phenocryst-type crystals.

Lunar Pebble This stereogram shows a pebble of lunar rock about 2.5 inches in diameter. The rounded shape as well as the bits of debris around its edge suggest erosion, despite the absence of water and wind. Erosional agents include the impacts of micrometeorites and differential thermal expansion stresses at lunar sunset when the temperature rapidly drops from almost 250° F. to −250° F.

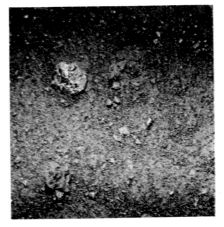

Lunar Glaze The small feature with a glass-like coating appears to be a .5 inch lump projecting from the moon's surface and not a loose piece of debris. It is possible that the thin, glassy material is the result of a tremendous outburst of radiation from the sun that glazed certain surface areas, probably within the last 100,000 years.

CRYSTAL SYSTEMS

 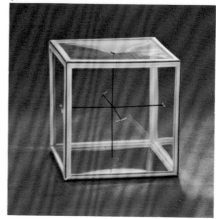

Cubic Crystal System   The crystal forms belonging to this system have three axes of equal length. The axes intersect at right angles. The system is also referred to as the *Isometric Crystal System*.

Tetragonal Crystal System   The crystals in the tetragonal system have three axes—two of equal length and one that is either shorter or longer. The three axes intersect at right angles.

Hexagonal Crystal System   This crystal system is the only one whose crystals have four axes. Three axes of equal length intersect on one plane at 120° angles. A fourth axis of a different length intersects the three at 90° angles.

Orthorhombic Crystal System   The crystals in the orthorhombic system have three axes, each a different length. The three axes intersect at right angles.

 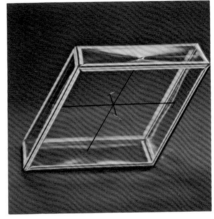

Monoclinic Crystal System   The three axes of the crystals in this system are of different lengths. Two of the axes intersect at right angles, with the third axis oblique to the other two.

 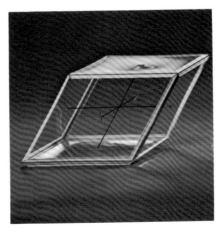

Triclinic Crystal System   The crystals in the triclinic system have three axes of different lengths. None of the axes form right angles, each being oblique to the other two.

INDEX

A

Actinolite, 45
Agate, 50
Albite, 50 (see also Moonstone)
Alexandrite (see Chrysoberyl)
Amazon stone (see Microcline)
Amethyst, 59
Andesite, 10
Anorthite, 51
Anorthosite, 8
Apatite, 40
Aquamarine, 54
Aragonite, 34-35
Arsenopyrite, 27
Asbestos (see Crocidolite)
Augite, 44
Autunite, 40
Azurite, 36

B

Barite, 38
Basalt, 10
Bauxite, 30
Beryl, 44 (see also Aquamarine; Emerald)
Biotite, 47
Borax, 37
Bornite, 24
Breccia, 12

C

Calcite, 32-33; "Iceland spar," 32; pink, 33
Carnotite, 41
Cassiterite, 30
Celestite, 38
Cerussite, 35
Chalcedony (see Agate)
Chalcocite, 23
Chalcopyrite, 25
Chlorite, 48
Chlorite schist, 19
Chromite, 31
Chrysoberyl, 55
Chrysocolla, 43
Chrysolite (see Olivine)
Chrysotile, 48
Cinnabar 25
Citrine, 49
Coal, 16
"Cobalt Bloom" (see Erythrite)
Cobaltite, 26
Colemanite, 37
Conglomerate, 12

Copper, 22
Coquina, 15
Corundum, 28 (see also Ruby; Sapphire)
Crocidolite, 46
Crocoite, 39
Crystal systems, 62-63
Cubic crystal system, 62
Cuprite, 28

D

Diamond, 54
Diopside, 44
Diorite, 7
Dolomite, 35

E

Emerald, 55
Enargite, 27
Epidote, 43
Erythrite, 39

F

"False topaz" (see Citrine)
Felsite, 7
"Fire Clay" (see Shale)
"Flos-ferri" (see Aragonite)
Fluorite, 32
"Fool's Gold" (see Pyrite)
Fossils
  in coquina, 15
  in limestone, 14
  in sandstone, 13
  in shale, 14

G

Gabbro, 8
Galena, 24
Garnet, 56
Garnet mica schist, 18
Gneiss, 19
Goethite (see Limonite)
Gold, 22
Granite, 6
Granite porphyry, 9
Graphite, 23
"Greenstones" (see Chlorite schist)
Gypsum (mineral), 38
Gypsum (rock), 16

H

"Heavy Spar" (see Barite)

Hematite, 29
Hexagonal crystal system, 62
Hornblende, 45
Hornblende schist, 18
Hornfels, 20
Huebnerite (see Wolframite)

I

"Iceland Spar" (see Calcite)
Igneous rocks, 6-11
"Iron mica" (see Biotite)

J

Jade, 57
Jasper, 50

K

Kernite, 37
Kyanite, 42

L

Labradorite, 51
Lapis lazuli, 58
Lava, 11
Lazurite (see Lapis lazuli)
Lead (see Galena)
Lepidolite, 47
Limestone, 14-16;
  coquina, 15;
  fossiliferous, 14;
  oolitic, 15;
  travertine, 15;
  tufa, 16
Limonite, 31
"Lodestone" (see Magnetite)
Lunar rocks, 60-61

M

"Magnetic pyrite" (see Pyrrhotite)
Magnetite, 31
Malachite, 36
Marble, 20
Marcasite, 27
Metamorphic rocks, 17-20
Mica schist, 18
Microcline, 52; amazon stone, 52
"Millstone Grit" (see Sandstone)
Mimetite, 39
Monoclinic crystal system, 63
Moon rocks, 60-61
Moonstone, 58
Muscovite, 47

N

Native Copper, 22
Native Gold, 22
Native Silver, 22
Nephrite (see Jade)
Novacekite, 41

O

Obsidian, 9 conchoidal fracture, 9
Olivine, 42
Oolitic limestone, 15
Opal, 59
Orthoclase, 51 (see also Moonstone)
Orthorhombic crystal system, 63

P

"Peacock Copper" (see Bornite)
Pegmatite, 6
Peridotite, 8
Phyllite, 17
Porphyry, granite, 9
Psilomelane, 30
Pumice, 11
Pyrite, 26
Pyrolusite, 29
Pyrrhotite, 25

Q

Quartz, 48-50;
  agate, 50;
  amethyst, 59;
  citrine, 49;
  jasper, 50;
  rock crystal, 48;
  rutilated, 49;
  smoky, 49
Quartzite, 20

R

Rhodochrosite, 34
Rhodonite, 46
Rhyolite, 10
Riebeckite (see Crocidolite)
Rock crystal (see Quartz)
Rock gypsum, 16
Rocks,
  igneous, 6-11;
  lunar, 60-61;
  metamorphic, 17-20;
  sedimentary, 12-16
Ruby, 54
Rutilated quartz, 49
Rutile, 29
  in quartz, 49

S

Sagenitic quartz (see Rutilated quartz)
Sandstone, 13; fossiliferous, 13
Sapphire, 55
Scheelite, 42
Schist, chlorite, 19; garnet mica, 18; hornblende, 18; mica, 18
Scoria, 11
Sedimentary rocks, 12-16
Serpentine, 19
Shale, 13; fossiliferous, 14
Siderite, 33
Silver, 22
Sinter (see Tufa)
Slate, 17
Smithsonite, 34
Smoky quartz, 49
Sphalerite, 24
Sphene, 43
Spinel, 57
Stibnite, 26
Stilbite, 52
Sulfur, 23
Syenite, 7

T

Talc, 46
Tetragonal crystal system, 62
Tiger's Eye, 59
"Tin Stone" (see Cassiterite)
Titanite (see Sphene)
Topaz, 56
Tourmaline, 57
"Trap Rock" (see Basalt)
Travertine, 15
Tremolite, 45
Triclinic crystal system, 63
Tufa, 16
Turquoise, 58

W

"White iron pyrite" (see Marcasite)
"White mica" (see Muscovite)
Wolframite, 41

Z

Zincite, 28
Zircon, 56